The **STU** Book

by Lynn Maslen Kertell
pictures by Sue Hendra and John R. Maslen

Scholastic Inc.
New York • Toronto • London • Auckland • Sydney • Mexico City • New Delhi • Hong Kong • Buenos Aires

Sipping squirrel   Tipping teapot

Unopened umbrella

Skunk and squirrel sail down the slide.

Snail slithers.

A tiger tickles tiny toes.

Tasty!

Unused umbrellas tumble,

scuttle, and flutter.

Tiger takes his turn. Terrific!

"Stop for a sip of tea," urges squirrel.

Look for these **s**, **t**, and **u** words in this book.

sail	takes	toes
sip	tasty	turn
skunk	tea	umbrella(s)
slide	teapot	unopened
slithers	terrific	unused
snail	tickles	urged
squirrel	tiger	
stop	tiny	
	tipping	

Look for these additional **s**, **t**, and **u** words in the pictures: sandwiches, steps, stripes, suitcase, table, tails, teacups, teddy bear, tent, tongue, trees, trumpet, unicorns, and unicycles.